ISBN 1 85854 606 0
Published by Brimax Books Ltd, Newmarket, England, CB8 7AU, 1997.
Printed in France.

Teddy's SHADOW

By Sue Inman

Illustrated by Roy Trower

Brimax · Newmarket · England

Teddy's Shadow

It was a sunny day. Teddy was walking through the meadow. Then the sun went behind a cloud and Teddy noticed something was missing.

"Oh no!" he cried out loud, looking at the ground. "I've lost my shadow!"

So Teddy began searching for his shadow. After a while he met Rabbit who was fishing by the lake.

"Have you seen my shadow?" Teddy asked Rabbit. "I've lost it!"

"No I haven't, Teddy, but I think..." began Rabbit.

But Teddy was in too much of a hurry to find out what Rabbit thought. Off he ran, searching for his shadow. Then Teddy passed Squirrel's house. He was in the garden.

"Have you seen my shadow?" Teddy asked Squirrel. "I've lost it!"

"No I haven't, Teddy, but I think..." began Squirrel.

But Teddy was in too much of a hurry to find out what Squirrel thought. Off he ran, searching for his shadow.

Next Teddy met Mouse who was feeding the ducks.

"Have you seen my shadow?" Teddy asked Mouse. "I've lost it!"

"No I haven't, Teddy, but I think..." began Mouse.

But Teddy was in too much of a hurry to hear what Mouse thought. Off he ran, searching for his shadow.

Teddy was still searching for his shadow when the sun came out from behind the cloud. Then he noticed his shadow was on the ground again.

"I thought you were lost!" said Teddy. Just then Rabbit, Squirrel and Mouse caught up with Teddy. Now they could finish telling him what they thought...

"...You'll find your shadow when the sun comes out!" they all said together.

Who will Play with Teddy?

On Teddy's birthday, his Grandma gave him a beautiful new kite. Teddy couldn't wait to play with it, but it was raining.
So when Teddy woke up the next day to find the sun shining he didn't even wait for breakfast. He put on his sun hat, took his kite and went out without saying goodbye to anyone. He went to Squirrel's house and knocked on the door. When Squirrel opened the door Teddy said, "Would you like to come and play with my new kite?"
But Squirrel took one look at Teddy, screamed loudly and slammed the door.

So Teddy went to call on Rabbit instead. But when Rabbit saw Teddy he screamed loudly and slammed the door, just as Squirrel had done.

"What is wrong with everyone today?" said Teddy to himself.

Teddy decided to try Mouse. He knocked on the door.

"Mouse, would you like..." Teddy started to say, but he didn't have a chance to finish. Mouse took one look at Teddy, screamed loudly and slammed the door.

Teddy began to cry.

"What have I done wrong?" he said.

"Why are my friends being like this?"

Teddy walked home with his new kite
which he still hadn't played with.

When Mother Bear saw Teddy coming up
the path she threw her arms in the air.

"Oh, you poor little bear!" she cried.

Then she whisked Teddy off to bed.

"What's going on?" asked Teddy.

But before Mother Bear could answer
there was a knock at the door.

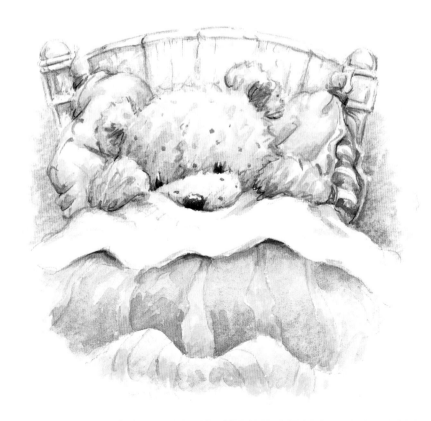

Teddy could hear his friends talking to Mother Bear downstairs.

"Have you seen it?" asked Squirrel.

"It's horrible," said Rabbit

"A big, spotty monster!" said Mouse.

Then Teddy heard Mother Bear's voice.

"You silly animals!" she said. "You haven't seen a monster! That was just Teddy. He's caught the measles."

Now Teddy understood what had happened. Rabbit, Squirrel and Mouse weren't really being unfriendly. They thought he was a monster because he was covered in spots! Even though he had the measles, Teddy felt much better all ready!

Can you find five differences between these two pictures?